# PATHS
# THAT
# CROSS

# PATHS THAT CROSS

by ESTHER DANIELS

Illustrated by Robert Pious

FRIENDSHIP PRESS                    NEW YORK

TYPE:  *Text, Baskerville 12 pt., leaded 4 pts.*
     *Display, Lydian*

COMPOSITION, PRINTING, AND BINDING: *Sowers Printing Co.*

DESIGNERS: *Format, Barbara Knox*
     *Binding, Louise E. Jefferson*

1074144

*To*

*The Edith Gramig Junior Circle*

*at Hope Church*

# CONTENTS

# A Story Without a Beginning

Every time Bayi walked the sandy beach path to Market Town, he watched carefully at the crossroads for certain tracks. If the Okak boys had already passed, he breathed a sigh of relief.

Bayi was a beach boy. Like other beach tribe boys along his coast of Africa, he had been taught that the Okak people were unfriendly. Bayi's father warned him from early childhood to avoid the Okak boys, just as Bayi's grandfather had warned Bayi's father when he was a boy. Back beyond anyone's memory, beach people had hated the Okak families, who were their neighbors.

9

When Bayi and his friends carried dried fish and cassava to Market Town, they had to cross the place at the river where the Okak path crossed the beach people's path. Often they discussed the possibility of an unfriendly encounter.

"Okak boys are savages." The boys all knew that.

"They are mean and cruel." They knew that, too.

"They fight with clubs." This was information the beach boys had only recently discovered. They learned it from examining the footprints at the path crossing. They often found an unmistakable warning in the sand.

"You see that long groove they make with a club every so often in the sand? It's a threat to us beach boys," they said.

The peculiar marking in the moist sand told the beach boys to make no mistake about Okak strength.

"They'd jump us from trees. They say the Okak people eat monkey meat."

"The way they look at us at the market place, you can just tell they'd love to catch us alone."

"They'd crash our skulls in."

"Let's carry bigger clubs, just in case." So Bayi and his friends now carried clubs and felt more secure.

Even so, Bayi always approached the crossroads with caution and fear, especially if he happened to be alone.

One day the thing he dreaded came true. Someone was

**10**

there, waiting. When Bayi saw the Okak boy, it was too late to run. He calculated the Okak's first move.

Bayi watched this boy, crouched there on the path, waiting. Was he a decoy? How many giant Okak boys would spring from the bushes?

What was that crying sound? This could be a trap.

With his club gripped hard, Bayi moved closer. He noticed spilled oil-palm kernels all about. Suddenly, the Okak boy sat bolt upright. He looked terrified. Bayi wondered if the Okak boy could be afraid of him. He drew closer.

"You spilled your load!"

"I fell," replied the boy.

Bayi stooped to pick up the scattered yellow palm kernels. He began to reload the basket as if it were his own.

"It's not the spilled load that gives me grief," the small boy moaned. "It's my crutch. My new crutch is broken. It caught in that deep hole there and broke when I fell."

"You walk with a crutch?" Bayi's eyes widened with surprise. "Then you don't carry a club!"

"What?" asked the puzzled boy. But Bayi didn't reply. He was staring at a shriveled, crooked leg.

"Does your leg hurt much? You were crying with pain."

They stared at each other. Then abruptly the crippled boy pulled the toppled basket toward him with his broken crutch.

11

He looked up at Bayi with a sheepish grin. "To tell you the truth," he confessed, "I guess I wasn't crying with pain. I was just scared. I knew you terrible fish-eating beach boys were soon to pass."

Bayi busied himself with the palm kernels and wondered how in the world this all began.

*※ ※ ※*

The stories in this book show some other paths in Africa that cross today. They tell about new experiences young Africans are having as, for the first time, they are becoming acquainted across tribal and regional barriers. The news items that follow the stories—many of them reproductions of actual clippings from papers and magazines African teen-agers are reading today—go further. They prove that the interests of people everywhere are very much alike, that the paths of more and more people both within Africa and beyond are crossing today. The stories and clippings also point out new responsibilities facing the church in twentieth-century Africa. They show opportunities that open up new paths for African Christians and Christians from other countries to follow together.

# I'll Be Back with More

"I say, Pierre, are you wanting to sell your cocoa this season or next?" Pierre was so engrossed in what he saw down the street that he didn't hear a word the trader said.

"You-from-the-hills, are you just going to sit there forever staring?" The busy trader who bought raw cocoa beans in the West African town called Bipindi was annoyed anyway with the half-size sacks of cocoa beans that the hill boys carried.

The youngster next in line gave Pierre a shove. Pierre bent his knees under the forty-pound burlap-wrapped load, eased it up, and quickly carried it to the scales.

Pierre's real name was Amugu. However, he preferred the French name this genial trader friend had given him the previous cocoa season because he could never remember the name Amugu. Older Bipindi boys often adopted foreign names, so when the trader called him Pierre in front of them, Amugu felt grown. Pierre was thirteen. His home was in a small village called Memel on the other side of the hilly forest and across a big river.

"Now," scolded the trader, "have you fallen asleep again? Am I to lift your load and pay you, too?" Pierre snapped to attention, freed the scales for the next boy in line, and opened the cocoa sack. Then he scattered the contents in the bin slowly while the trader's assistant watched with practiced eyes for hidden stones, which dishonest boys sometimes used to weight their loads.

"I'll be back later for my sack of salt," Pierre called, too excited about what he had seen to wait for the salt the trader would give him as pay for his cocoa beans. He was already outside the store, craning his neck in the crowd. He pulled his red felt beret from the hip pocket of his shorts, used it to swish off the dust from his stomach, and then absently placed it on his head. He scarcely heard the trader call after him, "Don't forget I close at noon."

Pierre deserted the other Memel boys and ran toward where he had last seen the two white-helmeted French boys. He elbowed his way through the people. He was

**14**

determined to see more of the boys' new red foreign wagon with just two wheels that he had seen gliding up and down the street with splendid ease. He cut through the food market, guessing the white boys who owned the wagon had circled the square. He tripped over a basket of tiny red tomatoes, and the vendor woman screamed after him. He ran head-on into a stack of bread, which fell, leaving the sputtering merchant too busy for chase.

Pierre spotted the French boys on the far side of the plaza. There he plunked himself on the curb and stared. They were taking turns, one foot at a time having a ride. Those two bright wheels spun in the sun. How smoothly they turned! Each wheel had a rubber tire!

From a discreet distance Pierre examined every detail with admiring eyes—everything, from the vehicle's low-slung platform with the blue stripe along its edge to the tricolor streamers that snapped in the breeze from each rubber-tipped handle. He noticed the brake that could slow the glide with a slight pressure of the rider's heel.

Eventually, from a sprawling, vine-covered, white man's house, a youth wearing a servant's apron appeared.

"Come!" he commanded the boys. "Your mother calls."

Pierre watched the red scooter disappear. Then with a stick he traced two circles in the dry dust along the curb.

"Wheels . . . platform . . . steering post . . . there!" Suddenly he noticed he was sitting full in the sun. The shadow in which he had sat down had shrunk in the noonday sun.

The market was almost deserted. Even the chickens for sale in their braided baskets were asleep along the stalls, and the long-robed, traveling merchants were napping by their loads. Was it siesta time already? Pierre suddenly remembered his salt and his waiting friends, and ran with all his might.

He could hear the click of the shutters being closed as he neared the trader's shop. The bolts clanged in their places. He turned the corner. The last shutter was being closed.

"I'm here. I'm here for my salt," he called. A long grumble greeted him, but he knew without being told that he was lucky. He would get his salt.

"Your friends got tired of waiting for you," the trader said. "They left an hour ago."

"Thanks a lot. I'll be back with more cocoa," Pierre assured him on the run. He must catch up with the other boys who were probably resting beyond the first river.

But Pierre's village friends had tricked him for deserting them. When he didn't find the other Memel boys or their loads at the rest house beyond the first river, he was frightened.

A glance at the sun told him if he hurried he might cross the next strip of forest before sundown. Perhaps

16

he'd catch up with his friends before nightfall. He felt terribly alone. There wasn't a soul in sight. The doors of the village houses he passed were all closed, so Pierre knew that people were still out working in their gardens. Village farmers don't rest by the clock as do the traders at Bipindi. As Pierre hurried through the villages, just the goats stood nodding under the overhanging mat roofs.

The wide, bare, pebble path of the last little town became only a jagged trail as it entered the forest. Accustomed to the heat of the afternoon sun, Pierre felt a sudden chill in the cool forest air. How he wished for his friends!

He was not afraid of getting lost. He knew every twist of the path to his home. It was being alone that was awful. Familiar forest sounds seemed exaggerated. Even the lines of soldier ants on the march crisscrossing the path seemed to murmur in warning. A monkey suddenly scolded him from a tree top and made Pierre quicken his steps to a run.

Up the hot steep climb, he paused only to adjust the twisted leaf buffer that helped him balance the load of salt on his head. He looked forward now to the cool rushing waterfall in the valley he knew was ahead.

When he took off his shirt and refreshed himself in the pure shower of the forest waterfall, Pierre started to

17

think again about the scooter. He untied the leaf bundle of rolled cassava-paste bread that he had forgotten to eat before and sat chewing great mouthfuls and retracing in his memory the mechanics of those spinning wheels.

As Pierre set his feet to the path again, he was scarcely aware of the forest. He had forgotten to be afraid. In fact, a distant thumping sound had been going on some time before he noticed it.

*Thump-ump, thump-ump, thump-ump.* It was the sudden staccato pause that froze his feet in their tracks. *Thump-ump.* He knew the sound. There was another pause before Pierre remembered what he had been taught. Walk calmly on, as though hearing nothing.

"Just walk calmly on." He could hear his uncle's words on a former journey. "Animals don't usually harm people unless they are first provoked," his Uncle Amugu had said. "Unless a gorilla has been injured, he will not come near."

Pierre swallowed hard and walked straight ahead. He never hastened his steps nor turned his head to look. The thumping sound soon died away in the forest. The male gorilla, having picked up Pierre's scent, was thumping his broad hairy chest in a kind of gorilla bravado. The gorilla had been just as frightened as Pierre.

The next day back home in Memel, the boys seemed overly eager to be friendly. Their fathers had roundly scolded them for breaking the first rule of the forest, deserting a member of their party. The boys thought Pierre was unnecessarily aloof.

"What are you making?" they repeatedly asked.

"What are you going to use the saw for?" The church elder's son was curious.

"I'm making something," was all that Pierre replied. He didn't want to sound too sure.

The wood of the *aseñ* tree was strong, yet light in weight. Pierre chose the roundest ten-inch log he could find. He sawed two identical cross sections about two inches thick, judging their width approvingly with squinted eye while the inquisitive gang stood by.

19

With his strong pocketknife, he hacked the bark from the edges and then he smoothed them down. He gave them a final sanding with the rough leaf of the "sandpaper tree," the same way he cleaned his wooden slate in school. The fellows barraged him with advice.

"Sure, you're making a scooter. I saw one once."

"I know a boy who made one, but the wheels split," another said. "You have to strip the wheels with iron."

"No, I'll tell you what is better," offered still another.

"What do you know about it?" someone replied in scorn.

Others, with no mechanical advice to offer, merely snorted, "It won't work," and left. But for the first time in his life, Pierre was the most popular member of his crowd.

So with mounting enthusiasm, he plunged ahead. The *aseñ* post for the steering rod he carefully carved down to size. Just below the place where it fitted through the wide platform, he designed it to bulge so as to hold the platform in place. The platform became the brace for the rear axle, and soon Pierre had the wheel turning freely in its groove. Around the wheels he carefully nailed strips of old auto tire that he had begged from the village shoemaker. The stripping, as he had been told, lessened the danger of splitting and protected the wheels from uneven wear.

20

The whole village was talking about Pierre's scooter. He found himself with more friends than ever, and they outdid themselves with advice, some of it helpful and some of it bad. Children ran errands for him in order to win a ride. Pierre paid them in test runs across the wide, open village. The boys argued incessantly about whose advice had really been followed and about how many rides one sound piece of advice was worth.

After the first model was completed, Pierre was still dreaming up improvements. The scooter was great on level stretches but impossible on hills and turns. It was bulky and too likely to spill. Pierre took the whole thing apart, reassembled it with minor changes, and then finally remade it altogether. He strengthened the front axle with an extra support. It was a completely new model. Now the little children cheered when they saw that he was adding a platform seat over the rear wheel. They argued about which one of them should have the first ride on it.

"Why should anyone stand to ride?" old men had asked from the start. That had set Pierre to wondering why two couldn't ride as easily as one.

On the day the new scooter whizzed by Uncle Amugu's house with two youngsters riding high, Pierre's uncle looked up and remarked, "Maybe that boy will settle down now that his toy is made. He's done nothing but play all week."

21

"Kids aren't as smart about work as they used to be," replied the shoemaker.

Pierre learned a lot about mechanics before he was through. Once a nail splintered the outer edge of a fine smooth wheel. As a temporary measure he whittled the wheel down almost half, and, much to his satisfaction, the smaller front wheel made the whole scooter more maneuverable. He installed a drag brake, but it ripped off the rubber tire. So he learned that a brake had to be applied with care.

When the scooter was all painted and done, Pierre's hardest job was a matter of salesmanship. Village adults only laughed when he said he would haul cocoa to Bipindi on it. He coaxed for two days before his uncle agreed to trust a whole sack of cocoa to the vehicle.

"Go ahead then," the old man finally said. "Wear yourself out carrying a man's load of cocoa and that fool machine, too. You'll just have to learn for yourself that wheels will never climb these hills."

So before his uncle could change his mind, Pierre divided a large sack of cocoa in two portions, each one as large as the one he normally carried on his head. One portion he lashed to the lower platform with bushvine. The second he balanced like a cushion over the seat. In a bundle tied on behind, he had some cassava bread for his lunch and clean clothes that he would don just before he got to Bipindi. This time he would not look like an ordinary country boy in town!

Pierre set out before dawn, and, much to his surprise, he found the group of market-goers that day the largest of the season. Boys who had no cocoa left to sell appeared with baskets of chickens and ducks. They were all eager to see what would happen.

Pierre gave his loaded scooter a running push and headed out through the village. When he reached the incline at the headman's house, he carefully eased himself up onto the seat padded with the cocoa sack, without slowing down. The scooter slid easily in swift descent with its squeaking wheels making dull thudding sounds as they moved over roots and ruts in the path that led to Bipindi.

Although his friends on foot easily caught up with him on the hills where Pierre was forced to push and teasingly passed him as they hurried to the top with their head loads, the scooter rumbled swiftly past them going down the other side. Always, whenever that happened, the crowd cheered in glee.

That day, in the trading town of Bipindi, two white-helmeted French lads stood staring bug eyed. The rumbling, redwood-powder stained scooter with indigo trim—and homemade tricolor streamers flapping the breeze—was a handsome sight to them as it entered town. They envied the African boy with the homemade scooter that was built for two.

Pierre's trader friend grinned as he looked over the scooter. "Before I know it, young Pierre here will be putting my trucks out of business," he said in fun.

"That's right, sir," Pierre promptly replied. "That's my big ambition, to own a fleet of real cocoa trucks." He added, "I'm sure some day there'll be a motor road over the hills."

Pierre proudly adjusted two sacks of salt on his scooter and retied a live turtle he had found at the river on top of his bundle of clothes. As he headed out of town toward the hills, dozens of necks craned for a view of Pierre's scooter. The pet turtle craned its long neck in return.

Next cocoa season it was the Bipindi trader who stared. Pierre's Uncle Amugu arrived in town pushing two large, man-size sacks of cocoa on a new model, Memel-made scooter!

# Sun and Moon

At first Jop hated the city and Ngon liked it. Jop missed his village friends, but Ngon, his sister, was fascinated with the busy city streets and the shops.

In a few weeks the opposite was true. Jop had new friends who had asked him to join their gang. Ngon felt more and more alone. The crowded streets seemed terribly lonely, and Jop didn't seem to know his sister existed any more. This made life quite different. Jop and Ngon were twins, and until now they had always stuck together.

One day Jop, whose name meant Sun, tore out of the tin shanty, which was their home in the city, tucking a new knife in his belt as he ran. Ngon, whose name meant Moon, watched him dodge an oncoming truck and wished her mother were at home. She was scared.

Ngon listened to the strange babble of their neighbors' voices. In shacks all along the crowded street, strangers from many tribes cooked and slept, quarreled and laughed. Babies cried. Women scolded. What was there for a girl to do all day? Ngon picked up the hot sheet of rusted iron roofing that lay in the sun and placed it against the entrance. She propped it with the brick and slab and left home to roam the streets for the day.

At the corner the vendor woman's golden corn cakes were frying in an iron pot of yellow palm oil. The bubbling, hot oil hypnotized Ngon. She felt terribly hungry. The oil was beautiful. The frying cakes in the bubbles of oil were beautiful. The blue enamel plate where glistening cooked cakes drained and tempted passers-by was beautiful. Back in the village Ngon's mother had cooked corn cakes in palm oil. Here in the city a single bottle of the rich yellow oil was costly, too expensive for her mother to buy. Ngon's stomach whined and ached for corn cakes —just one small corn cake would taste good. The vendor woman would never know. She would not miss it, and she could never find Ngon again in the crowd.

"Hunger, hunger. The city is hunger." Ngon's stomach told her so.

"Take me, take me. I am yours." The fat yellow cake near the plate's edge seemed to speak.

When the vendor woman turned her back to measure out meal in a bowl, Ngon quickly picked up the cake and disappeared. In a shaded corner of the market, she swallowed it almost whole.

Life here was different from their first twelve years. Jop and Ngon had lived then in a world full of just their "family." They had never known a day of hunger in all their lives. In their family village, the tribe was all the world and all the food of their growing gardens belonged in common to their family tribe. Every man in the village was their "father," and every woman their "mother." Even their fears and sorrows, their joys and pleasures were shared by all the village. Everyone danced or everyone mourned. Life had been just that way.

Things really began to change for the twins when word got around about the big hydroelectric dam that was being built along the Sanaga River. Workers were attracted by the high wages. Old men in the twins' village talked of nothing else but how times were changing and young men were leaving for the city. Those who did not get work on the dam usually found jobs at the new aluminum plant that was being built or in other cities along the railroad. Some stayed in the city and never returned to live again in the village. Others sometimes returned to visit but soon left again for the city. Always the village fathers sat around talking.

To make matters really complicated, not all the village men were against this turn of events. You might have thought that all the older men would naturally want the young men to stay and tend their gardens and herd their cattle, but this was not so.

The whole country was split by opposing political parties that promised new and better life for all. Formerly, people had tended to think of themselves as belonging to a certain family or village or section. They had not thought of themselves as being Africans. The emotion known as patriotism or love of country was just being born in this section of Africa. But, although Jop and Ngon had lived in a remote village a long way from such centers as Edea and Douala, they had heard during their childhood plenty about the poverty of their country and about the deep divisions among their own people.

One political party sided with the governing white men about how freedom should come about. Another party campaigned for immediate independence, crying, "Africa for the Africans. Out with the white man!" Most of all, many people just wanted quick money for better homes and things they knew other people had.

Jop's and Ngon's father was one of those who had gone off to work on the dam project, at first leaving his family behind. For weeks and months they were not sure where he was. Then one day their mother said their father had sent for them to come to the capital city.

Ngon remembered now, as she wandered along the street, how happy she had been that day. To think they would ride on a train!

While waiting for the train, Ngon's disappointments began. They had slept on the dirty station floor, guarding their baskets of squawking chickens, their bundles, and other baskets of food and clothing, pots and pans. The train ride had been miserable. Before ever reaching the city, Ngon had hated it.

Ngon hadn't even gotten to see out the train window. She had been almost smothered in the crowded coach. What was worse, she had been nauseated all the way. She didn't care where they stopped, just so they got off that train. When they finally flopped down to sleep in the shack where their father took them, Ngon was glad.

"We'll find a better place soon," her father promised.

Now months had passed since that train ride, and the baskets of food they had brought with them had vanished. The chickens had been eaten or sold. The money that the twins' father received on pay day never lasted until the next. Ngon's mother was constantly complaining about the misery of their shack. Her father often came home loud and drunk.

29

"Go earn your own money," he had shouted when Ngon's mother had cried. "To keep my job I have to support the Campaign. I must pay my dues every week. What's left for hungry kids?" he bellowed.

So the twins' mother now left for work every day at dawn. She worked with a crew of women, carrying sand and gravel for the new addition to the airstrip nearby.

Ngon kicked the curb with her angry heels. She hated all these people. She hated the flood of foreign sounds that engulfed her. She hated her father for being cruel to her mother. She hated her mother for leaving her alone. She hated Jop for having friends. Ngon hated the whole, mean, crowded world.

She waited there on the market curb, listening for the noon whistle of the factory. For her it meant the time of day when market women covered their wares and lay down to rest until the hot hour of noon would pass. It meant, as Ngon had learned, that then she could more easily snatch bits of food or fruit, sometimes even hunks of meat that she took home to cook over a small open fire in the shack at night.

All at once, plain and clear amidst the jumble of languages in the market place, she heard familiar words. A voice nearby was speaking her own language. She saw a white woman with a pleasant smiling face talking rapidly to the clerk at the vegetable stall.

30

"Well, hello there, my Bulu daughter," the woman said when she noticed Ngon's rapt attention. She paid for her vegetables and turned to Ngon.

"How are you this nice day?" the white woman asked.

Ngon was too shy to answer, but she tagged along beside the woman as though she were her mother. The friendly woman kept talking at a great rate and never seemed to think it strange that Ngon was following her.

After a while Ngon looked up timidly. "I will carry your load," she said.

"Thank you," came the reply. "It's a hot walk to the mission, but it isn't far. Are you going in that direction?"

"Yes, ma'am," Ngon heard herself reply.

The missionary lady was different from most of the other white women Ngon had seen in the city. Not once did she scold her for hanging around nor threaten her when she followed.

After that Ngon looked forward each night for the morning. Day after day she appeared at the bright green door of the small, cement-block house that had a flower bed out front. This was the place people called "The Mission," and it was almost in the heart of town. Always the lady told Ngon something interesting and new, and she gave her things to do. With the bright thread she gave her, Ngon copied in the corner of her headcloth the cross-stitch rose that girls at the mission embroidered. And

for weeding the flower bed at odd hours, the understand-ing Bible teacher's wife was glad to give Ngon garden vegetables or rice.

Ngon enrolled in the vacation Bible school that met in the chapel. How amazed she was to find that at least a dozen Bulu-speaking girls her own age came there every weekday! When she entered the chapel each morning at nine o'clock, Ngon took her place with the girls and boys who sat according to the languages they spoke. Over to the left sat the Douala-speaking children, at the right, the Basa, and in another section the Bafia. The superinten-dent was an African. Ngon learned that he was teaching still another mixed language group in French. Each teacher interpreted to his own class the story that the superintendent told in French.

After the lesson they all sang lustily. They listened to stories from the Bible, and they played games.

They also watched the work camp project. Thirty-five

32

boys and young men from thirteen different tribes were helping to build a recreation room near the chapel. After the work campers finished for the day, Ngon helped the women of the church serve rice and hot soup to them. Then they sang songs and played games. Following these, the workers talked about their work and the problems of Christians in the new Africa. Ngon listened eagerly.

One day the superintendent called Ngon aside.

"Where do you live?" he asked. "Do you have any brothers and sisters?"

"I have a brother," Ngon replied. "But please don't send for him. His friends would only laugh at him if he came near the white woman's school. My brother Jop doesn't know that I come." Ngon's heart skipped a beat. Was he going to send her home?

"Well, now," the superintendent said, "aren't you rather selfish? Your brother might enjoy the work camp project, and so would his friends."

"They only enjoy each other," said Ngon.

"But they might enjoy this," the superintendent insisted. "It's a lot of fun. You have seen it. We want to complete the foundation within a week, and then we will build the walls. Tell your brother we can use him. It's important that we get the roof on before the rains come."

On her way home Ngon thought over what the superintendent had said. Why hadn't she thought this through before? If Jop would go with her every day to the mission, it would be like old times back home in the village. Life had been fun doing things together.

"Before the rains come," Ngon kept saying to herself as she hurried along the street where the rusty shacks with their tin-can roofs exposed a lot of sky.

"Before the rains come, the roof must be on the recreation room!"

When she found Jop at home, she scarcely stopped for breath. "And after the rains come, there will be games and picture shows and singing in the recreation room," she concluded.

"Right now I'd rather eat," Jop grumbled as he kicked the dead firewood under the cold soup kettle.

Then he heard his sister add casually, "At the work camp there is rice and hot soup every day for the helpers."

"You mean it?" he asked.

"Come along with me tomorrow, and I'll show you," Ngon challenged.

"I'll drop by with the gang," retorted Jop. "D'ya think I'd want the fellows to see a girl leading me by the hand?"

Next morning Ngon met two girls from her Bible class, and they walked together all the way to the mission.

"Lucky for me that Jop has his own friends to come with," she thought. And suddenly Ngon knew that joys do not have to be forever the same.

# Without Hammer, Saw, or Nail

Ava was glad something different was going to happen. Even though he often helped his father gather building materials, this time it would be more interesting. Ava had volunteered with boys and men of his village to help build the new church. He hurried to morning prayers at Elder Noa's house. This particular morning he surely wanted to be on time.

During the prayers, which seemed longer than usual, he stole a glance around to see if the other boys were there. Everyone was there. It came Ava's turn to pray.

"God bless this church we will help to build."

"Amen!" quickly added Avebe, who was Ava's best friend. Avebe was anxious to get started.

"Amen," concluded Elder Noa. Ava and Aveba rushed for the door before older folks could turn around. A few minutes later, when the workmen gathered at the site selected for the new church, Ava and Avebe were already there, scuffling boisterously with other boys in fun.

Elder Noa took a piece of twine and proceeded to measure off the plot of ground. Ava received a sharp cuff from his father for tripping over the measuring line.

"What do you think you're here for?" Ava, the senior, scolded.

"Where's your cutlass? All you boys here without tools! Go get your cutlasses and hoes. There's work to be done!"

Ava's sister Edima and the other village girls had been hanging around to see what was going on. Suddenly, Edima heard her mother call. Now all the girls scurried in a dozen directions to their mothers' kitchens.

"Do you stand out there idle this morning? There's food to cook for the men. Go fetch fire and do your regular chores," said her mother. Edima obeyed, sulking out the door toward the nearest kitchen where blue smoke drifted up through the mat roof. She avoided the kitchen next door where a great puff of white smoke billowed from the doorway, for that meant their neighbors were only starting their morning fire.

Edima was accustomed to the boredom of being a girl. Today she would tend the baby. She would shoo away the hawks from the baby chicks. She would crack squash seeds by the endless hour. And today she guessed she'd also have to shell a lot of peanuts and grind them for the church workers' evening soup. And, of course, she must always keep pushing the three long logs under the simmering kettle. She looked forward to the one big day when the girls could help at the church.

As the leveling work began at the church site, a self-appointed leader struck up a chant. His voice burst forth in a question:

"Oh, why have we come to this place today?"

The chorus was ready with a reply, responding in the way men did when working in groups:

"To build God a house
 A house in which to worship God,
 To build God a house
 We'll build it strong and well."

Over and over questions were asked, and again and again the replies echoed while hoes and cutlasses moved to the rhythm of the chant.

Only three or four tools are commonly used for building in the central African forest village called Bidi. These tools are the wedge-shaped iron ax, the common broad-bladed cutlass or machete, and the long pocketknife. For leveling the ground after clearing, the boys used short-handled garden hoes.

Now the ground was almost leveled. The excitement of working together speeded things. Elder Noa supervised the staking out of the church. It would be thirty-five feet long, fifteen feet wide, six feet to the horizontal timbers, and twelve feet to the ridge pole.

"To the forest!" Elder Noa gave the order. This was the moment! Yet Ava knew that he and his friends must try to restrain their exuberance. Grown men would not tolerate rowdy youngsters on forest jobs. If Ava and his friends accompanied men on men's jobs, they must behave accordingly.

They entered the forest single file. From the edge of it behind the village, they wound their way through scarcely visible animal paths into the deep forest where they would find the termite-proof hardwood trees. The *éwomi* tree, found in the upland forests and hills, supplied the wood that they always used for the framework of buildings.

The men located a large tree and marked it to be worked another day. This would be split into long poles, using wooden wedges and their axes. They selected and cut four straight uprights a little over twelve feet long to support the ridge pole and thirty shorter ones nine feet long to make the studding.

"Now get the bark off those poles clean," Elder Noa ordered the boys, pointing to the four straight uprights.

"What did you say we do, our father?" a youth sang.

"Build the Lord a house," came the reply.

"How did you say to do?" asked the leader.

"Build it strong and well, build it strong and well."

The motion of cutlasses made a rhythmic scraping sound as the bark was peeled away.

When the poles were ready, each man and strong boy balanced one on his head, sometimes steadying the load with his hands. Eyes straight ahead and bodies erect, they set their feet in the direction of home.

"You two there, both of you to this pole," said Noa. Ava and Avebe gladly shared a load.

It was almost dark when they stacked it with the others near the cleared church site. Ava sniffed the evening air in anticipation. He knew the kind of thick, meaty peanut soup his mother and Edima had prepared.

The following day workmen were divided into groups assigned particular tasks. Elder Noa himself went in search of the very tall *ôjobe* tree, slender and straight enough to serve as ridge poles, plates, and braces. The *ôjobe* grew near rivers, so Elder Noa had not chosen the easy job. He waded swamps, river bottoms, and thickets until he was satisfied with the six trees necessary for the main supports of the little church.

Other men were assigned to bring in quantities of vine to be used for tying. They went to the uplands for the *minloñ* vine, which they patiently cut in lengths twenty to forty feet long, the vines being from one-fourth to one inch in diameter. Another group went to the swamps to gather the raffia palm canes that would serve as rafters.

This took several days, and then there were several days more when Ava and Avebe thought there wasn't anything especially exciting. The men just sat in the village under the eaves of the elder's house, splitting the vine into quarters or eights, according to size. They scraped and peeled the strong cane and made it ready for use, curling the finished lengths in convenient bundles in such a way that the individual strands could be pulled one by one, never disturbing the bundle.

Finally, the materials being all at hand, the actual building began. Ava had sharpened his cutlass so often he had no trouble whittling an upright to a sharp point. While the men and older boys dug holes for the thirty uprights that were to make the studding, Ava and Avebe scooped out the loose dirt with their hands. Each upright was carefully notched at the top with a V-shaped notch into which the plates, the horizontal timbers that support the lower ends of the rafters, were lashed securely to each with vine. The cross binders and the braces were likewise tightly lashed into place with strong vine.

40

Then the raffia palm canes were tied in their places with still more abundant use of vine, and the church began to resemble a real building. It was solidly framed, straight, neat, and plumb. Ava stood with the men as they judged the framework of their church and nodded with the rest that it was secure against even the worst storms.

While the framework was under construction, another crew went to the swampy forest to gather the long sword-like leaves from the raffia palm. While still in the forest, they stripped the fresh leaves from the canes in the patch and tied the bundles into individual cone-shaped loads, ready to be carried to the village. Ava and the boys were dispatched to bring their share of the leaf loads.

These long, slender raffia palm leaves were used in roof mats—the floppy, giant shingles that covered all houses in forest villages like Bidi. Mat-making was by far the most tedious job in building.

"One pile of ten, two piles of ten, three tens—" Ava kept counting the piles of finished mats and thought there would never be enough to roof the church. Furthermore, the men had decided to make the individual mats with double leaves to insure strength and long wear. The finished roof was also to have double layers of mats. That meant twice as many palm leaves were needed, twice as many mats as ordinary houses required. But Ava knew that a roof made like this would last five to six years.

Most fourteen-year-olds like Ava were not famous for their careful mat-making. Besides, men sat around and talked as they worked the leaves, and it was only when an interesting folk tale or animal story was told that the boys enjoyed this kind of talk.

Roof mats were made by first taking two strips of the outer coating of the palm cane and placing them parallel on the ground from six to eight inches apart. Over these strips the individual leaves were folded and pinned together with tiny slivers of the same cane fiber. It was tedious work, done by the men.

When enough mats were prepared, men climbed to the framework of the roof and lashed each set of mats to the rafters with vine, leaving only about three inches to the weather in evenly spaced, overlapping shingles. Down at the eaves the mats were allowed to extend several feet beyond the walls as protection.

The most exciting day for the boys and girls was still to arrive. Up until this time the bare double lathing made the walls quite transparent, making them look more like a basket than a building. The strong framework now stood ready for mudding! It would be filled solid with mud.

Ordinarily, this was a job exclusively for women and girls. But building the church was different. Everybody helped with the mudding, and it was a riot of fun. No matter how much they splashed and sloshed ankle deep in

42

the shallow trough where the mud was mixed, they would not be scolded. In fact, tramping the mud was essential, and many feet must stamp it fast to keep up with the throwers. Women and children carried the soft mud from the trough in old basins and baskets to the crew of throwers. Women and children carried the soft mud from women and boys did the packing of the walls.

Ava was first assigned to water carrying. This was disappointing. It took him away from the fun.

"Sissy job," muttered Ava.

"Women's work," teased Avebe each time Ava returned with a gourd of water.

Finally, Ava was promoted to carrying mud. That was more exciting. Scooping it up from the basin and carrying it to the base of the growing wall, he plunked it down with a heavy thud. Then the mudding crew scooped it up with their hands and threw it into place. Many hands packed it smooth so the laths no longer showed. They did this inside and outside until the walls were filled and firm. The finger-marked patterns on the west wall glistened in the afternoon sun.

Still the church was not finished, but it could be used. Split logs were arranged in rows for pews. Gradually, the damp odor of drying clay disappeared, and in a few weeks the walls now shrunken and patterned with cracks were ready for sanding. Ava carried many loads of river sand as his final assignment. Then, on the day men took slabs and plastered the fine moist sand over the cracks, the church again looked smooth and square.

Finally, at the beginning of the sunny dry season when rains would not mar the new finish, the church was made ready for the dedication service. *Fem,* the gray-white clay found in the creek bottom, was mixed with water for whitewash. When that dried, the church stood white and beautiful in the gleaming Bidi sun.

During the dedication prayer Ava thought he spotted the very pole he and Avebe had brought from the forest!

## Seeing Eyes

Elizabeth, the new missionary pastor's wife, was puzzled by what she heard. "Are you sure poor old blind Magip intends to trade his only daughter in marriage for a younger child?"

"Many customs in this part of the country will seem strange to you," the patient local African evangelist named Evina replied. "Remember, Christianity is new here while in the part of our country where you have worked before it has been changing lives almost a hundred years."

"I know," Elizabeth said, "but I can scarcely believe

that pathetic old blind father means much harm. His young daughter Mandougi is all that he has left in the world."

"Don't pity him; pray for him. But pray for Mandougi even more," the evangelist sighed.

"You mean, then, that when Mandougi is sent to her marriage it will not be to a man of her choice but to a man with other wives who can offer Magip a younger girl in exchange?"

"That's the old Baliama custom, and Magip is still a heathen."

"So, it's not a suitable husband for his daughter that is important but another girl to do his hard work, one who would be a convenient exchange!"

"That's customary," said the evangelist. "Later, if someone wishes to marry that girl, he may exchange her in the same way. Thus, he'll always have a gardener and cook. It's a kind of security for his old age."

"A strong worker is more useful in one's old age than goats or money," nodded Elizabeth. "But how unjust for the girl!"

"Ah, that's the problem," concluded Evina.

The village of Baliama lies in the broad, grassy plains. Pocketed off in a broad, shallow valley, the town is notorious for its resistance to change and its ancient *juju* practice. *Jujus* are beads or leather pouches or other objects

46

used to keep away evil spirits or to put curses on other people.

Nevertheless, there is now a Christian church in Bali-ama and, because of this, village life has changed in many ways. Today a girl like Mandougi might even dare to attend a young people's conference. It was, indeed, a district young people's conference that changed Mandougi's life.

This was the first time the Baliama church had offered to be host to such a gathering, and the people outdid themselves in the joyous activity of getting ready. Whether they approved of young people's affairs in the church or not, the congregation pitched in. In a single week the walls of the old crumbling church were repaired. School boys drew geometric patterns in bright dyes on the newly sanded walls. Days in advance women and girls began cooking, and kitchens were well stocked with food for the guests.

Mandougi was careful not to show any outward interest that might arouse her father's wrath. She deliberately waited on him more than usual. When he cursed the goings-on, she never uttered a word but more regularly than ever brought firewood to the kitchen. Blind Magip could know that she did this because he could hear her as she stacked the wood against the outside wall of the kitchen.

47

On the day before the conference began, the cooks made huge white corn-meal rolls and prepared pots of meaty soup. Old Magip also ate white corn-meal rolls, which he dipped in Mandougi's well flavored soup.

The conference welcoming committee didn't overlook a thing. They lined the path for miles with braided palms and arched them over the road. The arch they made at the chapel was festooned with yellow flowers.

People turned over their houses for guest rooms, and the young people swept them clean. Extra bamboo beds were brought in to accommodate the crowd. Plenty of firewood was brought to the kitchens, and for every log that Mandougi brought quietly from her own woodstack she ran a special risk.

Last, they swept the broad churchyard and then thronged the path to greet arriving guests. Guests were welcomed with singing and drums and rattle gourds. The school choir fairly burst the air with their much-practiced welcome song. Even the teacher was glad they had skipped algebra for weeks to practice for the conference.

Mandougi planned her day carefully. She would pretend that she was going to the garden. It would be easy enough she had thought. She would rise before daylight as usual. And old Magip would hear her start the fire. He would hear her rattle the iron pot and take her hoe and garden basket from the pegs on the wall.

She would go to the stream at the spring instead, and there she would bathe and dress. Her clothes were already in her basket on the wall.

"I go to get greens in the garden today, and I'll till the new corn," she said as naturally as though she really meant it.

"First you will bring me fresh water from the spring," Magip growled.

When she had brought the water he said, "Now you will rub my aching back."

Old Magip's various demands made Mandougi late to the conference sessions almost every day, but she heard enough so that she made a new decision—she would go to school in spite of anything her father said or did.

49

She learned many things at this conference. Young people almost everywhere were taking a real part in the church. She had always been content "to sit like a stone," just as the speaker had said.

Mandougi had never thought much about having a duty to her heavenly Father. She believed in God, but she had never before heard it said that loyalty to him should come first in one's life, come even before obedience to an earthly father. The speaker was careful to point out, however, that a Christian must be respectful and obedient to parents as long as this did not interfere with the higher duty.

During the discussion period, some asked a startling question: "Why did Jesus say, 'I came into this world, that those who do not see may see, and that those who see may become blind'?"[1]

The leader replied, "Jesus came so that men and women who are spiritually blind can see and know God with their souls in faith. Thus, he took away their spiritual blindness. He does this today. And people who refuse to receive Jesus as Savior make themselves spiritually blind, unable to see and know God, even though they have sight."

Mandougi was stabbed with this new thought. Could it

[1] John 9:39.

be that she was as blind as her father? She wanted to be a better Christian, and her first step would be to ask the missionary pastor's wife to help her go to the mission boarding school.

Blind Magip guessed his daughter's plans and became very angry. The day after the conference, he felt his way along the wall of his house until he touched the long bamboo pole that stood in the corner. Then he called loudly for Mandougi. She easily guessed what he planned to do when he said he would go to the trading center at Dang. But she grasped the other end of the pole and, obediently as always, became his seeing eyes.

A blind person's pole in Africa is a very effective instrument of navigation if a sympathetic guide is at the other end. Being rigid, it communicates the seeing one's least change of pace, the path's slightest incline or sudden turn in direction. The sight of the pole also gives sufficient notice on a narrow path for others to step aside or on a motor road for a driver to take special care.

Old Magip was quite a walker; he loved to go to Dang. Frequently, when he stopped en route to rest, he heckled the Christians. Magip hated them and didn't mind telling them so. He took pleasure in arguing with the mission people whom he suspected had put ideas in his daughter's head. Mandougi was often embarrassed, especially when her father had the bad taste to ask the pastor's wife for a gift. Still there were some Christians who believed he would change some day, and missionaries like Elizabeth were unsuspecting and kind to him.

This trip Mandougi knew was made with evil intent. Magip's anger over the conference would make him seek revenge. He would plant an evil *juju* in the hand of the pastor's wife. He did not know Mandougi had seen him wrap the eggs he was carrying.

"I must warn her. I must warn the pastor's wife," Mandougi kept saying to herself and, without uttering a word about her thoughts, she determined never to go back home. Quickly, quickly, quickly. Her heart pounded out her fear. How could she warn Elizabeth in time?

When Mandougi and Magip rounded the corner at the mission bookstore, the old man began to curse everyone he met. His voice grew louder and louder as they climbed the path toward the pastor's house. Some people scolded and argued back. The commotion warned Elizabeth that the old blind man was on his way to the mission to call on her.

Mandougi led her father to the edge of the veranda. Usually, they waited there together, Magip cursing others who were also waiting. But this time Mandougi didn't wait on the veranda. She ran immediately to the back porch. The pastor's wife listened to her excited words with puzzled surprise.

"The eggs. Don't eat them!"

"What eggs?" Elizabeth asked.

"The eggs he gives you. Don't eat them! Don't eat them!" Mandougi gasped. She was so excited that she could scarcely speak.

"My dear girl," Elizabeth asked, "what in the world are you talking about?"

"The eggs are poisoned," she panted.

"I see," laughed Elizabeth. The girl must be hysterical. Old Magip had never been known to give her or anyone else a gift.

"That can't be," Elizabeth said, calm as she could be. Just then she saw the cookboy approaching hastily from the front porch, bearing an object over a stick at arm's length. He shook his head and muttered loudly. Elizabeth saw what seemed to be the usual egg cluster, a half dozen or more eggs wrapped individually for carrying in dried banana leaves and tied conveniently in a cluster. It was a typical gift for an African to present to the missionary pastor's wife.

Elizabeth's cook obviously was not receiving this particular gift of eggs in the usual gracious way. Before Elizabeth could collect her thoughts, the cook entered the kitchen, holding the cluster of eggs aloft. Removing the lid of the stove, he flung the eggs into the fire, and slammed the lid back on.

"Well, that's settled," the cook announced with a loud sigh of relief.

"What's settled?" asked Elizabeth.

"I've saved us all from sudden death," he assured.

"All you've done is destroy the evidence."

"You think it's a joke." The cook's face was serious. "You don't know Magip. He wouldn't give a Christian a gift. We all know his power with *juju*."

"Oh, don't be silly. I can't imagine how it would be possible to poison unbroken eggs."

"Easy," he replied. "You take a long needle—"

"For pity's sake, stop! Mandougi and I have matters to talk over before I see Magip."

Mandougi hopefully told Elizabeth of her plan to stay on at the mission station and enroll in school.

"But if you come here to school, who will care for your blind father? Who will cook his food?"

Mandougi looked incredulous. This was not the answer she expected.

"Can't you try to go to school back home in Baliama?" Elizabeth felt that Mandougi simply had to try to do this for a time at least.

"But, ma'am," protested the girl in tears, "you don't know my father. He's a devil. Never in all my life has he permitted me to go to school. Look at me! I am now thirteen!"

54

"Nevertheless," urged the pastor's wife, "it would be better for your father if you could stay at home and care for him while you attend school. Isn't it better to try?"

"You haven't heard about the marriage trade?" Mandougi asked.

"Yes, Evina told me, but aren't you anticipating trouble before it actually happens?"

Elizabeth thought rapidly ahead as she talked. She felt sure the governor would never permit the illegal marriage trade, especially if the church stood loyally behind the girl. Yet she knew they had no case to place before the governor so far. You can't convict a man—even an old heathen like Magip—on mere hearsay, she told herself.

"Yes, Mandougi, I am sure." She looked the girl straight in the eyes. "You must go home and do all you can to be obedient to your father and be a Christian, as well," Elizabeth said.

As she left crying, Mandougi's eyes made her look like a frightened antelope. Yet they also said she trusted Elizabeth.

"You advised her cruelly," admonished the cook who had overheard.

"I know," replied Elizabeth thoughtfully. "Sometimes true obedience to two fathers requires really desperate loyalty."

Months later, freed by the governor from the illegal

marriage arrangements, Mandougi again wept but this time with a new feeling of mingled love and hope and pity for her father who was still blind of soul as well as sight. She watched the policemen lead him cursing from the courtroom. She knew, though, that her heart would ache even more than it did if she had not actually tried to be an obedient daughter.

## Surprising Things Happen

This was one morning when Kiku was sure he would win the race to chapel. He had run faster than the other boys. He was dripping wet and out of breath. But when he peered through the bleak dimness of the school chapel, there was Mono, first again and calm and collected in his usual place in the front row!

Most of the dormitory boys were later than usual for prayers that morning. It was raining torrents, and the pounding storm on the metal dormitory roof was so deafening that few of the boys had even heard the chapel gong. It was so dark, who would think it could be morning? Besides, the slick red mud of the schoolyard made haste dangerous.

"How does Mono do it?" the boys all asked when Kiku announced his failure to arrive first. They brushed the water from their heads and slid to their places along the chapel benches.

"Every morning, every day—how can a chimpanzee always win?" The boys decided they would try another plan.

Mono was more than the dormitory mascot. He had been the missionary's pet ever since the boys found him orphaned and starving in the brush outside of town. Mono was promised to a zoo in America. The price he would bring would help build the new church.

Mono preferred dorm life to the quieter existence in the missionary's backyard. So he was rarely confined to his pen. Of course, in the dorm he got plenty of attention from the boys and was a constant source of amusement.

But Mono's uncanny habit of always getting to morning prayers before the boys really had them stumped. Morning after morning they raced to be first. Always Mono would be there ahead of them. It was the superior look on the chimp's face that provoked them. After all, how much smarter than a schoolboy can a chimpanzee dare to be?

Sometime the boys would outwit Mono, perhaps when it was not raining so hard.

"I'll borrow the teacher's alarm clock," volunteered one boy.

"We'll sleep in our clothes," suggested another.

"Put our sandals right by our beds," added a third.

"Better still, why bother with shoes at all," said Kiku with a grin.

But whether they admitted it or not, the boys knew they had little chance of beating Mono to the chapel. The chimpanzee had discovered that the sound of the gong meant a dash to the chapel and also that the sound of the head teacher's footsteps just before the gong meant that the gong was about to ring.

This was Kiku's first year away from home, and these unexpected bits of fun in a boarding school dormitory made school life happier than he had anticipated. He had dreaded coming because he had heard from other boys about the poor food. Some said he would be hungry. As long as he could remember, boys had reported back home about schooldays with nothing to eat but plain boiled cassava. No rich meat gravy, very seldom peanut soup, and, certainly, they were never served the delicious palm soup with the fresh shrimp and fish their mothers cooked. When boys came home for week ends or vacations, they loaded up with delicacies and returned to school to stretch their precious tidbits as long as they would last.

But, aside from those predicted hungry days when the missionary often scoured the countryside for the variety of food boys need, there had been only pleasant times. Not counting exams, of course!

Kiku enjoyed the hilarity in the dorm at night. He got a lot of fun out of tricking the teachers and fooling around with the other boys. Yet, he studied enough to keep well afloat.

Soccer was his favorite sport; they called it football. Next best Kiku enjoyed the school plays and Bible dramatizations. These were often done on the spur of the moment without rehearsal following the lesson. Kiku had a flare for acting. Of course, all the students did, and this often lead to heated quarrels when, for example, six would-be kings insisted on playing Nebuchadnezzar.

On week ends Kiku talked so much about football and plays and how they tricked the teacher that his father often asked, "Don't you do anything in school except play?"

"What's to tell about arithmetic?" Kiku would reply.

One morning about midway through the term, Kiku opened his eyes later than usual. This time he didn't jump out of bed. He was sick; he had been ill all night. Now he felt feverish and dry. He closed his eyes again and lay very still. It hurt to move. Now he was floating away. Nothing was holding him. He was floating, floating.

When any of the schoolboys were ill, malaria was naturally thought of first. Especially in the rainy season, as now, more cases of malaria appeared than at any other time. Cool wet weather stirred up malaria in the blood, it seemed.

When the principal heard that Kiku was sick, he sent the dorm monitor to the storeroom to get a blanket. Students usually had only their lightweight, woven cotton cloth, which served as sheet, blanket, and wrap-around bathrobe. The limited number of soft warm blankets a church once sent the school were saved for just such times as this.

When the boys covered Kiku and asked him what was wrong, he did not reply.

During the morning the orderly from the mission dispensary made his rounds to check on dormitory boys reported ill. He saw that Kiku's illness was not ordinary. If it was malaria, it was certainly a severe case.

When Kiku failed to respond after the drink of liquid quinine usually given for malaria, the dispensary orderly called the medical assistant in charge. He in turn sent for Mrs. Smith, the missionary nurse. Meanwhile, the boys rolled Kiku over onto the blanket and carried him to the dispensary ward.

Mrs. Smith knelt by the low, bamboo dispensary bed and noticed the pale yellowish cast to Kiku's normally rich brown skin. She felt his fevered head and looked up at Afan, who had been her assistant in charge of the small mission station dispensary for many years. Afan had been trained by a missionary doctor, and, although he held no medical degree of any kind, it was only lack of formal training that kept him from being a full-fledged physician. There had never been a medical school for Afan to attend.

"Have you taken a blood specimen?" Mrs. Smith asked.

"Yes," Afan replied, "but I haven't had time to examine the slide. The lab assistant is away at his father's funeral, and I've been rushed with other patients."

"I understand," Mrs. Smith sighed. "Take charge here. I'll examine the slide myself." Every day this missionary nurse wished the mission had time to train more help and money to pay an increased staff.

As she entered the tiny laboratory where stood the single microscope, the rack of test tubes, slides, and assortment of bottles with the stains and other things, Mrs. Smith was struck anew with the meager equipment they had to work with in the face of so much need.

"If my friends back home knew how skimpy our equipment is, they'd be doing more about it through their churches. They'd be giving more money for missions." As she focused the lens, she counted the days until the missionary doctor would make his monthly visit. It would be almost a week.

As expected, the blood slide showed some malaria, but it was evident that malaria was not the cause of Kiku's fever. "Almost everyone in this part of Africa carries malaria all the time in his blood," Mrs. Smith thought. She knew that chronic malaria is one of the reasons so many Africans lack ambition and energy and that a boy like Kiku often suffers from several tropical diseases and parasites that sap still more strength.

She and Afan were soon sure, however, that Kiku had meningitis. He was now barely living, and with each hour his chances grew less. And it was five days until the missionary doctor would arrive.

A strange silence surrounded the school compound. Although there were classes as usual, each morning and evening Kiku's classmates lined up to have their temperatures taken and to report any physical ills. The missionaries were afraid others might have contracted the illness. It was neither headache nor fever that made Kiku's friends quiet; it was a heavy feeling around the heart.

They prayed for Kiku's recovery, and, in groups of six or eight each evening before bedtime, they stood as close to the ward where Kiku lay as they were permitted. They would sing an evening hymn and then quietly slip away.

Kiku's parents had come from their village to be near their boy, but they sat in mourning. They were sure Kiku was all but dead.

**63**

"The doctor would do a spinal, but will Kiku live until he comes?" Afan said. "His chances would be greater if I could go ahead. But I am not a certified doctor."

"I know," Mrs. Smith replied sympathetically. "It is agony to know what should be done, and even be able to do it well, but to lack professional authority to proceed. How I wish we had a real medical school in this part of Africa!" That wish had been expressed before.

No one thought it just plain luck or mere chance that brought the doctor a whole day early. The schoolboys said that their prayers had been answered. Kiku's parents called it a miracle.

As Kiku's strength returned, even Mrs. Smith had a strange feeling about him. Accustomed as she was to medical miracles, she knew surprises often happen. Yet, she told herself, this was no ordinary miracle of medicine. What had kept Kiku alive? Was it the sugar water she kept dropping between his dry lips hour after hour for want of the glucose they did not have at the little mission dispensary? Had this sustained his strength? At least it had satisfied her desire to do something to help. In her missionary career, Mrs. Smith had often known God to use small offerings to perform his miracles.

One evening weeks later, Mrs. Smith heard a cough at her front porch. She looked up to see Kiku with his parents, followed by a large delegation. She knew something important was about to happen. She never knew just how gratitude of Africans might be expressed. It could be they would sing a song. It might even be they would present her with a live, pure white goat.

"In Africa," she reminded herself, "surprising things happen."

Kiku's father's speech was long. Mrs. Smith was prepared to make her usual gracious reply. But this was an unusual thank you. Kiku's father wasn't saying thank you the way African fathers usually did.

"He was my son, but he is no longer mine," he said. "I gave Kiku up for dead. Indeed, in my heart I had already buried him, for I had no hope. Therefore, I no longer deserve to call him mine. So I have come to give him to you. Do you understand? He is your son now." With that he gently pushed Kiku toward her.

It was fortunate that Mrs. Smith quickly remembered another story of long ago. The words of Hannah in the Bible[1] came back to her as she deliberately returned Kiku to his father's side where she knew he belonged.

" 'For this child I prayed; and the Lord has granted me my petition. . . . Therefore I have lent him to the Lord; as long as he lives, he is lent to the Lord,' " Mrs. Smith repeated.

[1] I Samuel 1:27-28; 2:1.

Kiku's mother understood. She replied, saying, " 'My heart exults in the Lord.' "

" 'As long as he lives, he is lent to the Lord.' "

The crowd agreed, saying, " 'As long as he lives, he is lent to the Lord.' "

Kiku's parents had dedicated their son to God's service in the company of witnesses. But Kiku's personal commitment would gradually grow real in the school years ahead while he used his strong body and keen mind wisely in both work and play.

There came an evening when the dormitory boys heard Kiku say, "I'll beat Mono to chapel in the morning!" Then they all knew that he was really well again.

# They Discover Each Other

Marie Basama could hardly wait for her father to return with the mail. He was surely taking a long time to go to the post office. "Still," thought Marie, "it is better to be expecting mail than to learn it hasn't come." It would be another whole long week before the next mail day at Ngan.

"If I don't win a prize this time, I'll just give up trying the contests," she told herself impatiently.

But aloud she said to her mother, "The most exciting day in the whole month is the day the magazine *Discover* arrives."

A young man's voice piped up. "You think you're going to read *Discover* first, do you?" Nyem was Marie's older brother who had just come in the door.

"Why shouldn't I?" Marie contended. "You haven't entered the Big Contest, and I have."

"That's kid's stuff," Nyem replied. "I'm doing the Science and Life Correspondence Course for a certificate."

"Well, sure," sighed Marie. "But you're not so grown. We're both taking correspondence courses. I do the Bible Quiz Page every month. Today I'll do the second lesson in Acts. It's a new series, and this time they'll print the answers to last month's quiz."

"I know. I know. And after ten lessons on your own, they mail the exam. You aren't telling me anything new. I already have one Bible Certificate, you know."

"So then," concluded Marie, "more reason why I should get the magazine first this time."

"You two quit your arguing," their mother scolded. "You'll take your proper turns, after your father reads the News Page, of course." And then she added almost to herself, "As usual, I'll be lucky to read the Woman's Page last."

Dr. Basama, the father of Marie and Nyem, dumped the contents of the small mailbag in the middle of the floor. Nyem quickly dived in, scattering the mail with both hands.

"Take it easy there. That mail's not all yours." Dr. Basama always brought the mail for the hospital staff, and occasionally there were letters for patients as well. But that was not often, for all the patients at Ngan Hospital were lepers.

"Here, sort these letters." Nyem's father handed him a batch.

Marie recognized the folded, yellow-covered monthly with its bold blue stripe across the corner. She slipped off the wrapper and gazed at the bright color enlargement of a smiling African telephone operator. "The pictures are always wonderful," she thought.

Her heart fluttered a bit. Marie knew the contest winners would be printed inside the back cover. She closed her eyes a moment in anticipation, tucking her thumb between the cover and the last page. Then quickly she scanned the opened page. But her eyes didn't seem to focus. She looked closer. She stared.

There at the top of the Contest Page were the familiar prizes: the Kodak box camera, the two bicycles, and the fancy umbrella. There was the new jumbled line puzzle for this month at the bottom as Marie expected. But what was wrong? What had happened? Everything else was different. She could not read a word!

Seeing his sister already deeply engrossed in their favorite magazine, Nyem sauntered toward her in the way older brothers do and, with a flourish of pretended politeness, withdrew the magazine from Marie's hypnotized stare. "I thank you," he bowed.

Before she could say a word, Nyem was saying, "This is odd."

"What's odd?" asked their father who had now finished sorting the mail. He was just about to leave to deliver it before reading his own letters. Mail addressed to the mission at Ngan was not great in quantity, but it was certainly as precious as gold.

"Look at this!" called Nyem. He thrust the magazine before his father's eyes.

"Well!" Dr. Basama observed. "The local edition!"

"You mean in the language of the people around here?"

"Yes," said the doctor, "hadn't you realized? That's one thing that makes it special. It's published in different languages so more people can read it."

Nyem's mouth still hung open in surprise. "I thought *Discover* was printed only in English and French."

"It also is printed in three vernaculars," said the doctor as he went out the door.

"We must have gotten someone else's copy by mistake," moaned Marie.

Dr. Basama and his family were missionaries—not missionaries from Europe or America—but Africans who were missionaries from one country in Africa to another.

The doctor had specialized in the treatment of leprosy and in leprosy hospital management. He had received his training in a large mission hospital a thousand miles to the south of Ngan. He volunteered through his church when he heard of the need at Ngan for a specialist. His own church's medical committee then agreed to lend him for a while to the neighboring mission in order to help train a specialist of their own.

So, although the Basama family had never been outside their own part of Central Africa, they agreed to work and live up north among people they had always heard were quite different from themselves.

Many things had made leaving their own country difficult. First, their relatives had not liked the news that they were to move.

"Who will help with family emergencies with you so far away?" they asked. The brothers and sisters of Dr. and Mrs. Basama didn't approve at all.

"We'll never see you again as long as we live," the old grandparents sadly announced, crying over Marie and Nyem.

Hard as all this was, Dr. and Mrs. Basama's main concern was about their children. Would the schools be as good as the Christian schools they had always attended? Would it be hard on them to be suddenly uprooted and to adjust to a totally new environment?

71

For Marie and Nyem, leaving home had been an awesome experience. Although they did not cross a broad ocean, they felt they might just as well have done so when they crossed the two wide rivers that separated their own forest country from the grassy plains of the north. When they headed north, then west, through a part of the country where their grandfathers had never been, Marie felt as if her own world had broken away from her at the last river, leaving her alone and sad. Nyem remembered his grandfather had said the people across the river were a fearsome, warring tribe.

"Are we really going to have to stay there three whole years?" Marie moved closer to her mother as she spoke.

The first discovery Marie made at Ngan was concerned with language. She had been accustomed to different languages and had grown up understanding four tribal dialects besides her own. She also knew French and some English. But Marie had just never dreamed that the people of Ngan would be so completely ignorant of her own comfortable tongue, which she thought was very special.

The first day had been the loneliest day of her life. The doctor and his wife were busy unpacking and meeting people on the hospital staff. Marie just stood around staring, feeling utterly deaf and dumb. Girls stood staring at her, too, seeming to be equally deaf but not at all dumb when it came to their own kind of speech. They prattled to one another in a hideous foreign tongue. They looked her over. They giggled. Then they stared and giggled some more. It was awful. She remembered her friends back home that night and cried herself to sleep with her face in her pillow.

That was six months ago, and Marie still didn't have a real friend or pal. Although she was learning their language, the girls at school had their little cliques of their own tribal friends. Marie pretended to them that she didn't care.

However, the girls were never intentionally discourteous. In fact, Marie had never seen people more outwardly friendly. They greeted her and wished her well every time they met and parted.

The respect they paid their elders was surprising, and

their greetings were really a ritual. Marie had been taught back home to wait to speak to an older person until he had first spoken to her. Here, her mother explained, a young person must first greet the older person, saying, "May you live long." The older one would return the greeting with the blessing, "You won't die." When Marie discovered these greetings, she was impressed.

Soon she found that certain classes of people had their own special greetings. For instance, the weaver and the tailor at the hospital shop were greeted in one way, the hospital carpenter in another. The workman who climbed the palm trees on the hospital grounds to trim them or to gather the fruit had a different way of greeting Marie's father. Even circumstances altered a greeting. A person leaving the hospital for home was wished a special blessing. That was something her own people didn't do.

"Doubtless many careless youngsters nowadays disregard these traditional manners," Marie's mother said. "But, as guests of good will, we will do our best to learn these courtesies and follow them as graciously as though they were our own."

Language and new customs were not Marie's only surprises. She soon learned that in Ngan there were more Muslims than Christians. This made a difference. Here Christians were not always respected, and Muslims were sometimes openly hostile to them.

74

"Back home it was easier to be a Christian," Marie remarked to her father.

"Yes," the doctor replied, "because, when Christians live in a predominately Christian community, there is a feeling of family participation in all of life. Here, Christians don't mingle with the close-knit Muslim people who live behind those brown mud walls."

In Ngan, Marie couldn't distinguished a Christian from a Muslim by his dress. Back home she had always supposed people wearing heavy flowing robes were all Muslims. At least the Muslims she had known usually dressed like this. But here she found that the full embroidered garments of the men and the women's bright full prints were the time-honored tribal dress. Christians wore them, too.

Dr. Basama explained, "You see, the Muslims we knew at home generally had come from here in the North. That's why they seemed to us to look different."

There were regular times each day, however, when Marie had no trouble knowing who were Muslims. Five times a day the call went out from the high minarets of the mosque in the city square. Then Muslims washed themselves wherever they were and prostrated themselves in prayer. Even when beyond hearing distance, they knew somehow when it was time. In the market and on the streets, Marie often saw them perform their cleansing ceremony before they prayed. They took the small enamel teakettle they always carried and poured water over their feet, their arms, and their heads. Then they would bow in prayer.

At the mission hospital Marie discovered the kind of ritual that she understood much better. Christian prayers at Ngan were not so different from those back home! Before daylight each morning her father arose as he had always done and attended morning prayers with the staff. Often he would go down to the wards to the prayers held with the patients; this gave the lepers encouragement.

Marie often went with her mother to visit the Home for Untainted Children about a mile from the wards. She liked to play with the leper patients' children who were kept at the home because they were still free of the disease. She loved the smiling women who mothered the little ones, for they were just like the Christian women she had always known who worked in a Christian hospital.

"Each day I see someone who reminds me of someone back home," Marie remarked to her mother.

"People aren't so different," her mother replied.

Nevertheless, there was still resentment in Marie's heart. She missed her own good friends. She wished they had never come to Ngan.

"Marie," said Dr. Basama at breakfast the day after the mixed-up mail, "since you pass the post office on your way to school, suppose you return that magazine to the postal clerk."

"Why?" Marie whined. "It spoiled the whole month. I'll never know now whether I won the camera."

"Do as I say," her father said.

Marie fidgeted as she waited in the line at the post office. She would be late for school, and just for an old magazine she couldn't read! Maybe she'd just run on to school and throw it down some place on the way. Who would know? Still, her father might ask. She guessed she'd have to wait. Why do so many people need stamps and money orders today? Are people in no hurry at all?

The big man ahead blocked her view. She stepped aside to count the people before her. Something up ahead just naturally attracted her attention.

There, in a girl's hand was a folded yellow-covered magazine with a blue stripe across the corner! It looked just like the one she had.

Marie stared so hard, she didn't notice that she was being stared at, too. The girl with the other magazine lifted it above her head and smiled. Marie smiled back and waved hers. Then they both giggled. The other girl left her place in line and came back to Marie. They examined both magazine wrappers. They giggled again and stood awkwardly together in the line, continuing to giggle in excitement.

Suddenly, Marie grinned and shrugged her shoulders. The other girl grinned and shrugged her shoulders, too. Then they exchanged magazines, and together they ran out the door and down the street toward school. They had discovered each other!

As the two girls walked home together that afternoon, Marie realized a remarkable fact. Here was a girl in a long northern dress, who spoke a different language and had strange blue markings on both cheeks, and yet she was very proud to be this way. On the other hand, she herself wore a short dress, had no facial markings at all, and she, too, felt proud. Both read *Discover!* Both were Africans! Both were Christians! But most surprising to Marie, here they were, friends already!

# A Story Without an End

Several years ago a medical missionary named Reuben A. Torrey, Jr., went to China. While there he lost his right arm at the elbow. Back home in the United States, he was fitted with a mechanical forearm.

In 1952, after the Korean conflict, Dr. Torrey volunteered to go to Korea to help set up a rehabilitation center at Severance Hospital in Seoul for war victims who had lost an arm or leg or both. This rehabilitation program was sponsored by Church World Service, and thus Dr. Torrey became an interdenominational missionary, representing many churches.

As an amputee, Dr. Torrey was able to understand the problems of amputees better than the average missionary. He trained many Koreans to make artificial limbs.

But the story does not end there. One of the Koreans whom Dr. Torrey trained was Chung Kan Mo, who had lost a leg. He became an expert limbmaker and was sent to Europe to learn the latest techniques.

The Presbyterian Church in the Cameroun heard about Mr. Chung and asked him to spend a year in Elat, teaching doctors at Central Hospital to make and fit artificial limbs. There he started the first limbshop in that vast area of Africa and began teaching Africans to help their own amputees. So paths cross and crisscross, in Korea and Africa and around the world.

**Put life into your pictures**

All of us cannot go to Africa or even know personally any person born in Africa. A few may go to an African country to live or to visit, others may correspond with a teen-ager in Ghana or Nigeria or South Africa. Still others may meet a student or adult from Africa who has come to this country to study or carry out some assignment. All can read news about Africa in a newspaper any day, knowing that youth in Africa are reading the same news in their papers. Did you ever see a newspaper printed in a country in Africa? The pages that follow present clippings from such papers—*The Daily Times* of Lagos, Nigeria, *The Nigerian Tribune,* Ibadan, Nigeria, and *African Challenge,* an interdenominational Christian magazine. Comparable items might have been taken from papers in any part of Africa. You will also find clippings from two American papers, the Louisville, Kentucky, *Courier-Journal* and *Times.*

Africans have a sense of humor and definite views about us . . .

10     THE LOUISVILLE TIMES

# Things In 'Darkest America' Puzzle African Teacher

### Any snakes?

Some ask you whether Nigeria is in Kenya and whether you approve of the Mau Mau. All they read is about the savagery, cannibalism and poligamy of the African; the snakes, the jungle and the wild animals.

The woman who refuses to take you in may fear that, perhaps, you have snakes in your bag which you can release to attack her in dispute.

But, after all, the British are but human. If we discriminate against each other in Nigeria, just because we happen to come from different regions or speak different languages, what finger can we point at others without pointing nine to ourselves?

## Patrick Unogwu Speaks at U.L.

**By NORMAN SHAVIN**
Louisville Times Staff Writer

A native African teacher visiting here finds some things in Darkest America baffle him.

His reaction to some American customs and habits is much as yours would be to the "talking drums" and funeral dances of his native Nigeria.

Here are some of the things that puzzle Patrick Otokpa Unogwu, 21, who lectured yesterday at the University of Louisville:

"Americans are never satisfied. They always have to change things. This year's new auto is different from last year's. Television sets get bigger and bigger. But the programs are not good. I don't like them."

### Self-Adornment First

Young Americans seem strange to this man of the West African bush.

"Next to their own adornment, they like dancing best. In Africa, men and women do not dance together. They dance alone so that others will admire them."

## LAUGHLINE

*Vernon*

"THIS HURTS ME MORE THAN IT DOES YOU!"

views determined in part by headlines in their own newspapers.

**NO GOING BACK**

**SINGER PUNCHED ON STAGE**

**States attack civil rights Bill**

**NOT AN EASY JOB!**

**Hollywood's fixed idea of Africa**

**Negro girl student barred from classes**

**U.S. SENATE TO DEBATE NEGRO RIGHTS BILL**

Youth have their sports favorites and enjoy athletics . . .

# AFRICA'S YOUNG CHAMPION

## Hogan Bassey

★ KENYA: Thirty-six schoolboys in Kenya completed a three-week course of athletics and competitive games, which ended with a climb of Mount Kibo, the 19,000-foot peak of Kilimanjaro.

Miss Violet Odogu, the well-known Nigerian woman athlete. Her elegant poise and fine proportions are the result of constant exercise.

## ENCOURAGE PHYSICAL EDUCATION IN SCHOOLS

R. ANTHONY, Onitsha:

APART from a few Government institutions and private secondary approved Schools, very many of our schools and colleges do not employ physical training instructors.

their dreams go beyond today and their own countries.

## WORLD CUP IN 1960?

WILL Nigeria be ready to take part in the World Cup football competition in 1960?

That is a proposal which the Nigeria Football Association may consider after the English football team's

# SPORTSMANSHIP IS OUR GREATEST ASSET

Teamwork...

Nigerian Girl Guides are flying to the United Kingdom to represent Nigeria at the World Jamboree which will be held in England. More than 4,000 girls from other nations in the Commonwealth are also attending the Jamboree. The Nigerian Girl Guides will camp near Windsor Castle. Their leader told the "Sunday Times" at the Kano Airport that "the girls are all excited about the trip and are looking forward to meeting their comrades from other parts of the Commonwealth."

The Nigerian Contingent to the

## BOY SCOUTS WORLD JAMBOREE

leaves by air from Ikeja Airport to-day, July 20th.

# Each year new jobs in Africa call for trained young people . . .

opportunities for better education for more students are essential.

For good work—
you need good health!

HANDY BOYS OF LAGOS made these neat wooden mats, table tennis bats and rattle at the handicraft class.

## UK school boy to address Nigerian leper colony

NEVILLE DAWS, an eighteen-year-old schoolboy from Stourbridge in the West of England will sail for West Africa on Thursday to deliver a goodwill message to the Nigerian leper colony which was founded thirty-one years ago by his father, the Rev. H. H. Daws, now Vicar of Stourbridge.

Today problems, old and new, call for solution . . .

● When I grow up

## I want to be a Nurse

A GIRL may choose her life work from many professions, such as medicine, law, or teaching. Some professions pay much money, but some pay more in love and respect than in money.

When choosing a profession, one should not think of money alone or of making a living, but one should think of the help it will be to others and how it will improve one's community and country.

Nursing is my choice for a life work. To be a nurse is to be like an explorer, because nurses explore to know the human body and how to keep it working.

We know that doctors help sick people, but they only prescribe; and if nurses did not carry out the treatment, the sick people could not get well.

I like the work of a nurse because there are so many ways of helping the mothers in the villages where they cannot easily get to hospitals.

Jesus Christ went about doing good and helping the sick; so if we are His followers we should do the same.

When people are sick we have a wonderful opportunity of telling them about Christ, who can also cure their souls. That is why I would like to be a nurse. —FAITHFUL KEMMER

## PEOPLE IN BACKWARD AREAS NEED HELP

## Literacy awards for 1,760 adults in Aba area

THE CHAIRMAN of the Aba-Ngwa County Council Chief J. N. Wachuku, has urged educated young Nigerians to join the campaign to wipe out illiteracy in the country, so that by the time the country becomes independent, nearly everyone can become literate.

He said it would be a tragedy if Nigeria achieved independence with a majority of its citizens remaining illiterate.

## 'JUJU' RE-ECHOES

## SPINAL SICKNESS HITS ZARIA

TWO people have been reported dead in Zaria and nine others affected following an outbreak of cerebro-spinal meningitis.

A team of sanitary workers, led by Malam Sumaila Ahmed, has arrived in the town.

## Three die in 'trial by ordeal'

SALISBURY, Thursday

A "TRIAL BY ORDEAL" to discover the originator of spells and witchcraft is believed to have resulted in the deaths of three Africans near Chikwawa, Nyasaland.

## NEPU condemns juvenile delinquency

THE Plateau provincial branch of the Northern Elements' Progressive Union has condemned the high incidence of juvenile delinquency.

## Two more girls rescued from slavery

TWO more girls have been rescued

adequate preparation for careers that meet human needs is desired by many.

## CAREERS FOR — EVERY WEEK

### .. AND HERE IS THE FIRST

HERE'S the first career—a white collar newspaper job — a journalist.

What are the qualifications? A good general education is essential with preferably a West African School Certificate or Cambridge School Certificate—a good pointer to an adequate grounding.

Good English, of course, is essential, both in the spoken and written word, for journalists have to be able to talk to anyone, then express what they have learned in lucid, precise language.

Shorthand and typewriting are also of prime importance — Shorthand is needed for taking note of important statement or court hearings (which form a large part of the reporter's job). Typewriting also enables the journalist to put his thoughts down in a legible way so that the printing departments have no difficulties in transforming his reports or articles into newspaper form.

Most important qualifications of all are a lively mind and complete honesty — without these no journalist can reach the top.

And the top is very attractive. Salaries of well over £1,000 a year are common for top-class men and the way is often open to even wider careers. Just think of our Cabinet Ministers and others who were journalists first!

Training is usually on the job, first as reporter then later as sub-editor. Courses in journalism are offered in London and a college training scheme for journalists is likely to be started soon in Nigeria.

At the start, however, there is little glamour and little pay — around £15 a month; nor are there many jobs available. But for those who break in (a good way is to write articles and submit them for the newspapers) and make the grade the prospects are bright indeed.

or experience.

Part of the trouble is that many of our leading students look only to the white collar professions for a career and many others would hesitate to be an engineer or a craftsman.

Yet people who are not afraid of getting their hands dirty with hard work are the people most in demand. And often the best paid.

To help young people, soon to leave schools or colleges, to make up their minds about their career the "Sunday Times" will publish every week on this page a Careers Guide with details of jobs, prospects, sala-

### Watch out

ries and the training needed.

All sorts of jobs will be covered from hydrographers to ecologists and stenographers! Look up the dictionary to see what kind of jobs these are!

The Nigerianisation Office, the Department of Labour and other departments as well as commercial firms will be co-operating with the "Sunday Times." So watch this page every week for news — news that could determine your future career.

New nations are launching new projects that promise improvement . . .

# NEEDED TO CLEAR LAGOS SLUMS — £50 MILLION

**MR. J. W. HENDERSON**, Chief Executive Officer of the Lagos Executive Development Board has said that it would cost £50,000,000 to clear all the slums in Lagos by 1967.

Housing accommodation would be eased, rents reduced and a more congenial atmosphere achieved, he added.

## CREATE AID FUNDS FOR UNEMPLOYED

ALEX BOLANLE, Lagos:

I WANT the Governments of the Federation all to work together and solve the mass unemployment problem which is staring them in the face.

independence brings with it new responsibilities.

**Self-Government an important landmark**

**Tribalism in politics**

**Reds Offer Cash to All Africa, Asia**

**Official Hints Nations Seize West-Run Firms**

By The Associated Press
Cairo, Dec. 27.—The Soviet Union offered all Asian and African nations economic aid Fri-

**MORE YOUTH CLUBS PLEASE**

ONE of the Northern political parties wants the Northern Government to form more youth clubs in the region to combat increasing juvenile delinquency.

**Govt. should educate people on the evils of Communism**

**Labour leaders urged to show sense of mission**

THE Northern Nigeria Minister of Health, Alhaji Ahman Pategi, has called upon Nigerian trade union leaders to demonstrate a high sense of mission and a "spirit of give and take" in their fight for the welfare of workers.

**Why arm when we need money for development**

Constantly Africans are coming closer to one another and to people on other continents . . .

# GHANA SEEKS TRADE OVERSEAS

ACCRA, Friday.

THE GHANA GOVERN-MENT ANNOUNCED LAST NIGHT THAT IT WOULD SEND FIVE MISSIONS OVERSEAS TO STUDY TRADE PROSPECTS AND THE POSSIBILITY OF ATTRACTING FOREIGN INVESTMENT IN GHANA.

In a statement, the Ministry of

## Nkrumah welcomes Ghana's first merchant ship

TAKORADI, Wednesday.

# SUDAN PREMIER HOPES FOR RAIL LINK WITH NIGERIA

SAYED ABDALLA KHALIL, Prime Minister of Sudan and Minister of Defence, said shortly after his arrival at Ikeja Airport yesterday that the initiative for the proposed Port Sudan-Nigeria railway link came from both sides, and that although each country was expected to contribute its own share towards the pro-

# *ROAD WORKS TO BEGIN AFTER RAINS*

## NEW IKOYI ROAD WILL HAVE NEW BRIDGE

## New road to link British and French Cameroons

## SIERRA LEONE MINISTER TO TOUR NIGERIA

they are moving from a candlelight era to "Total" light.

Across Africa the Christian church is at work . . .

## RELIGION TODAY

# American-Run Church In West Africa
# Turned Over to Native-Born Members

### By GEORGE CORNELL
#### Associated Press Religion Writer

In a far-off land a white-skinned clergyman this week handed over a century-old charter to a dark-skinned clergyman. They shook hands and bowed their heads in thanks.

The job was done. An American-run church had become an African-run church.

"This is the realization of dreams . . ." the participants said.

Transactions of this kind have become a familiar feature of the world-wide Christian enterprise today, with the control of churches started years ago by foreign missionaries being turned over to new, native leaders.

*CHRISTIAN LITERATURE PARCELS* are just what pastors, teachers, and all Christians need to build them up in the faith. "I cannot express my joy at having such an opportunity to read the papers sent me each month," says one reader.

# Prayer asked for...

# THE 'PASTOR'

ARIBIBI OYEWOLE has been depressed for a long time and he attributes the cause to his sins. He asks ...vers so that he may be re-
... had ways and con-
...ARIM

A. ALANEME and wife request that prayer be said on their behalf so that they may be blessed with a child... FRANK OKOH who recently passed an examination asks for prayer of thanks to God.

teaching and worshiping, training leaders, meeting needs.

"Ye shall be witnesses unto Me . . . unto the uttermost part of the earth."

KNOWN as the Radio Pastor to many listeners in West Africa, the Rev. A. T. Olude believes in using modern methods to preach the 'old time religion.' He has been a Methodist minister for 21 years.

The possibilities of increasing the sale of Bibles and Christian Literature with the use of a Bookmobile are most intriguing. New literates are eager for books.

*The Drum Call*

# NEW NAME FOR BASEL MISSION CHURCH

THE Basel Mission Church in Southern Cameroons has changed its name to Presbyterian Church of the Cameroons and adopted a new constitution by which it becomes an autonomous institution.

The church can now prepare its own budget, train Cameroonians as ministers of religion and subsequently transfer administrative and executive responsibilities to Africans.

The Basel Mission Church, now known as the Presbyterian Church of the Cameroons is one of the oldest religious organisations in the Southern Cameroons. It runs a chain of churches and schools. Jointly with the Baptist Mission Church, it also runs a secondary school in Bali.

**TO FACE THE NEW SITUATION**
Where formerly the Christian school has often borne the major responsibility for education, nationalism calls for the secular governments to take control. Christian educators in Africa and Asia must build stronger Sunday Schools and youth groups in the local church.

Many Christians from other parts of the world are working with Africans, welcomed as partners in the building of new nations. More such friends will be desired and needed in the future. You can begin now to make your path cross that of some boy or girl in Africa by placing on this page stamps from Africa, an autograph of an African with whom you have talked, a clipping about Africa, a picture showing some work your church is doing in Africa. This may be your first step toward knowing better some person or group in Africa.